D1096295

A book for You

_____ ,

From Me

_____ ,

About Us.

ISBN 0-7683-2161-1

Compiled and illustrated by Kathy Davis
© 1999 Kathy Davis Designs
www.kathydavis.com
All Rights Reserved

Published in 2000 by Cedco Publishing Company
100 Pelican Way, San Rafael, California 94901
For a free catalog of other Cedco® products, please write
to the address above, or visit our website: www.cedco.com

Printed in China

1 3 5 7 9 10 8 6 4 2

This journal is dedicated
to
∘• Kathy Richards •∘
whose friendship has never faded
through the years or over the miles.

Our roots are deep
Our ties are strong.
That's why our friendship
Blooms on and on.

Friends are Flowers that Never Fade

a Journal

illustrated by Kathy Davis

Cedco Publishing Company . San Rafael, California

Dear _____,

　　Within these pages you'll find some of my thoughts and memories detailing something very special to me - .: our friendship :.
　　Although I'm sure I left some things out, and probably remember some things differently than you do, I hope that you enjoy reading my recollections as much as I did writing them.

Thanks for being such a wonderful friend!

　　　　　　　　Love,

　　　　　　　　_____

Our Friendship

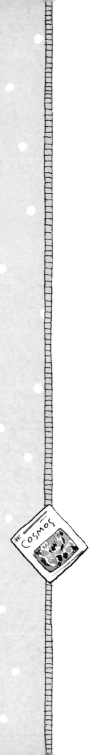

The Seeds of Our Friendship

We're such good friends because...

Ways we're alike

Ways we're different

Our Budding Friendship

How we met ....

....

....

....

....

....

....

....

....

....

....

....

....

....

....

We cannot tell the precise moment when friendship is formed. As in filling a vessel drop by drop, there is at last a drop which makes it run over; so in a series of kindnesses there is at last one which makes the heart run over.

James Boswell

One of the first things I noticed about you was...

....
....
....
....
....
....
....

Other Early Memories..

....
....
....
....
....
....
....
....
....

Remember when...

∴ Our Perennial Friendship ∴

Why we've stayed friends ....

....

....

....

....

....

....

....

....

....

....

....

....

....

....

....

....

....

∴ Treat your friends as you do your pictures, and
place them in the best light. ∴
                                    Jennie Churchill

Something I'll bet you don't remember is...
....
....
....
....
....
....

We really thought we were something when ....
....
....
....
....
....
....
....

Remember when...

Nurturing Our Friendship

Caring and Communication

You are a caring friend because...

The nicest thing you ever did for me was...

....

....

....

....

....

....

....

....

....

....

....

....

....

....

....

....

....

....

:• Gratitude preserves old friendships, and
procures new. •:
unknown

Something nice I'd like to do for you is...

I felt closest to you when...

A TRUE FRIEND is the Rarest of all Blessings.

· LA ROCHEFOUCAULD ·

Remember when...

Helping Each Other

One of the ways you've helped me most is...

He that does good to another does good also to himself.
Seneca

You taught me...

I taught you...

....

....

....

....

....

....

....

....

....

....

....

....

....

....

%• A little for you and a little for me -
This is friendship. •%
Indian proverb

NO MATTER WHAT

Something I learned about myself from you

You've helped me grow by..

It is one of the blessings of old friends that you can afford to be stupid with them.
Emerson

Friendship is a sheltering tree.

· Samuel Taylor Coleridge ·

I couldn't have done it without you

Thank you for...

....

....

....

....

....

....

....

....

....

....

....

....

....

....

....

....

....

....

....

....

.... I am wealthy in my friends
Shakespeare

Remember when...

Celebrating and Giving

Celebrations we've shared

A friend

will joyfully sing
with you
when you are on the mountaintop,
and silently walk beside you
through the valley.

Remember when...

Remember when...

Shared joy is double joy...

a friend
is a present
you give
yourself.

ROBERT LOUIS STEVENSON

The gift from you that meant the most to me was...

If I could give you anything in the world, it would be...

⚱ Our Blooming Friendship ⚱

The most fun I ever had with you was..............

....

....

....

....

....

....

....

....

....

....

....

....

....

....

....

....

Other fun times

:• Friends do not live in harmony merely, but in melody. •:
Thoreau

Remember when...

Probably the silliest thing we ever did was...

....
....
....
....
....
....
....

I still get a smile on my face when I think about...

....
....
....
....
....
....
....
....

Other Adventures

Blossoms
are scattered
by the wind
and the wind cares nothing

.. but the blossoms
of the heart
no wind can touch.

· YOSHIDA KENKO ·

My idea of a perfect way for us to spend the day

....

....

....

....

....

....

....

....

....

....

....

....

....

....

....

....

....

Remember when...

Remember when...

The better part of a man's life consists of his friendships.
Abe Lincoln

Best Buds

The qualities I appreciate most in you

....
....
....
....
....
....
....
....
....
....
....
....
....
....
....
....
....
....

Friendship

Why I cherish our friendship

Why I cherish our friendship

°° Hold a true friend with both your hands °°
Nigerian proverb

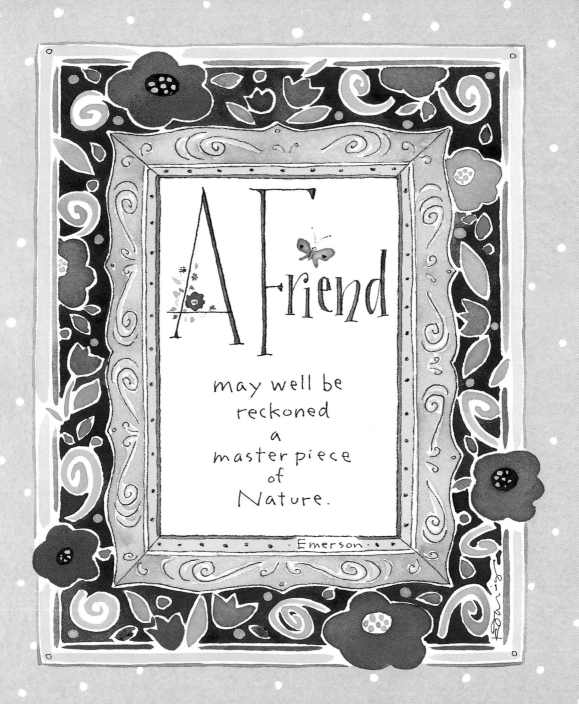

A Friend

may well be
reckoned
a
master piece
of
Nature.

· Emerson ·

I was so proud to know you when...

Ways I understand you that no one else can

Ways you understand me that no one else can

Although you know me almost better
than I know myself, you may not know...

....

....

....

....

....

....

....

....

....

....

....

....

....

....

....

....

°。 In my friend, I find a second self. 。°...
Isabel Norton

friend

One who knows
all about you
&
Loves you
just the same.

ELBERT HUBBARD

Remember when...

Friendship Potpourri

Ages and stages

Ages and stages

 A friend is someone who understands your past, believes in your future, and accepts you today just the way you are. ⚬ unknown

Remember when...

Don't walk in front of me.
I may not follow.

Don't walk behind me.
I may not lead.

Just walk beside me
and be

my

FRieNd

.unknown.

KDavis

Our rites of passage

There are those who pass like ships in the night, who meet for a moment, then sail out of sight with never a backwards glance of regret; folks we know briefly then quickly forget...

Our rites of passage

...Then there are friends who sail together through quiet waters and stormy weather helping each other through joy and through strife. And they are the kind who give meaning to life. °³ unknown

∴ Uniquely Us ∴

Things we've shared ....

....

....

other friends ....

....

....

books ....

....

....

songs ....

....

....

....

ANNUAL MIX

PORTULACA

ZINNIA

movies

....

....

....

inside jokes

....

....

....

nicknames

....

....

....

our "own language"

....

....

....

....

Other favorite memories..

. . . .

. . . .

. . . .

. . . .

. . . .

. . . .

. . . .

. . . .

. . . .

. . . .

. . . .

. . . .

. . . .

. . . .

. . . .

. . . .

. . . .   Two friends, two hearts, with one soul inspired...

Homer

My
treasures
are my
Friends.
·Constantius·

Our travels

Our travels

Wherever you are, it is your own friends who make your world. ❧ William James

Birthdays and special celebrations

Birthdays and special celebrations

....

....

....

....

....

....

....

....

....

....

....

....

....

....

....

....

....

Never shall I forget
the days which I spent with you...

Continue to be my friend,
As you will always find me yours.

·Ludwig van Beethoven·

Dates to remember ....

....

....

....

....

....

....

Other favorite memories ....

....

....

....

....

....

....

....

....

....

....

Notes & photos

Notes & photos

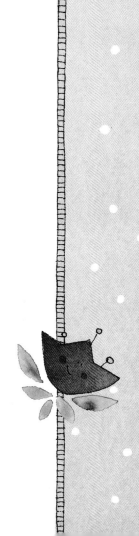

Remember when...

Old traditions

The road to a friend's house is never long.
Danish proverb

Setting new traditions

Things I want to do together someday

Future hopes and dreams

:. My best friend is the one who brings out the best
   in me. .: Henry Ford

:. The best mirror is an old friend .:
                              German proverb

Notes & photos

∵· I no doubt deserved my enemies, but I don't believe I deserved my friends. ·∵ Walt Whitman

Notes & photos

Notes & photos

Notes & photos

⁘ And the song from beginning to end, I found in the heart of a friend ⁘ Longfellow

other books
by Kathy Davis
from Cedco Publishing

✿ Friends are Flowers that ✿
Never Fade

☺ The Time to be Happy is Now
a Book of Inspirations

♡ An Address Book —
The Time to be Happy
is Now

When in the
Philadelphia area,
visit the original
Kathy Davis
retail store,
located in North
Wales.

Call (215) 661-8444
for information

Kathy Davis
COLLECTION

To order
Kathy Davis
products, visit our Online Store
at:

www.kathydavis.com

or call:
1·800·542·2797
for a
free catalog!

Help support
the following charities
by purchasing products from
our Online Store:

✿ Lady Bird Johnson Wildflower
Center
www.wildflower.org

☺ Buddy Dog Humane
Society
www.buddydoghs.com

Kathy Davis has always loved art. A former teacher, she designed her new career as an artist and writer one greeting card at a time. Her colorful style and uplifting messages now adorn thousands of products found worldwide. Kathy loves nature, and many of her designs reflect her favorite subjects of sunshine, flowers, and animals. Inspiration and humor often find their way into the original verse and quotations that adorn her creations. Kathy lives in the Philadelphia area with her family and a menagerie of pets.